Specimen Sight-Reading Tests

Piano

by Alan Ridout

Grade 3

The Associated Board of
the Royal Schools of Music

AB 2397

Gavotte: Moderato

Nocturne: Andante

Scherzando

AB 2397

16 Moderato

17 Andante

18 Allegro ma non troppo

31 Briskly

32 March

33 Waltz

AB 2397

Printed in England by Caligraving Limited Thetford Norfolk

7:97